CW00383701

For Gresley,
hope you enjoy it.

Vishu

TIME SECRET

1/37   £3.49

For Miranda,
hope you enjoy it!
Viqui

Time Secret

Viqui Rosenberg

Longstone Books / London / 2009

© 2009 Viqui Rosenberg

Longstone Books
19 Barnard Road
London SW11 1QT
www.longstonebooks.co.uk

ISBN 978-0-9554373-3-5

British Library Cataloguing in Publication Data
*A CIP catalogue record for this book is available from the
Bristish Library*

Printed by the MPG Books Group in the UK

CONTENTS

for my children Manuela and Miguel,
and for Carlos – friend and witness

ONE

Primal Scene

Let's start at the beginning.

There is a young Captain. He fancies himself full of promise. Like the country he fights for, he does not believe in the real. Real is ugly. He believes in the wonder of purely distilled blue blood. The excellence of blue can overcome all nasty manners of reality. Blue makes mother the most beautiful woman and father the most fierce man; blue makes him the hero of any story that he cares to tell himself; blue will help him to pay his debts; blue can hope for horses to win battles against tanks and it turns the colour of his own Jewish blood.

This he will tell me again and again: that against all the odds, blue blood runs in our veins. That I am not the Jew that girls reject or tease in the playground;

that I am some other sort of Jew, a blue Jew. So I do forget what exactly it is that sets me apart. Whether it is that I am too smelly, too poor, too proud, too clever or too Jewish.

Once in the new world, looking from his new life, the blue Captain is witness to the demolition of his country, the hunting and destruction of his family, his mother's vanity and foolishness when – from the ghetto – she writes that she cannot find lace gloves in the shops. This Captain gallops his horse from one influential person to the next to be told always the same thing: that his mother's destiny is different from his own, that she will crumble from hunger into silence, locked in the besieged city. He keeps his feelings very quiet because he is so shocked at this mistake. Whose mistake? I don't think he asks this. He continues to live his broken life.

There is the girl from abroad. The first one born away from the pogrom. It is a privilege to have a complete family to be born into. No one drowned at sea, no one stranded among enemies or lost for ever in the new world. Only one child taken by disease.

This privileged family wants to embrace the new world. Each child is to bathe in the glow of living in safety. Each child is assigned a hope: water-colours, violin, ballet, bank. La Rusita gets the piano. She hates sitting at the keyboard. She wants to know what is happening outside, what it is that the others are doing, whether anybody remembers her when they form the teams. She runs her fingers on the keys hoping to make time pass faster but the sound prevents her from hearing the world around her.

I can hear her father in the workshop, sweating over the saw. Yesterday someone came looking for a dining table. He had an instant of despair, then a moment of inspiration: he sold their large and beautiful table for ten, the one he had made when they first arrived. The family will eat on their laps until he finds time to make another one. Life is good and simple in this new world.

What she really likes is to go dancing. The music, the crowds, the way that men look at her, the sensuous and slippery conversation full of innuendo, the dreams. But the closest to the dance-hall that the parents will allow is University. In fact, they are delighted when she proposes it. Their own child, their very first in the family, the only one who has dared to think of it! Every effort will be made: La Rusita wants to be a doctor.

Wanting to be a doctor is as good as suddenly being five years older or being one of the boys or having your own money. Somehow it gets easier to go dancing. The older sisters resent her; the younger ones want to be like her; the brothers include her. She feels part of every team.

Saturday night. I don't know what time of year or what special occasion. Whether it is to do with University or with the Jewish community or perhaps with my eldest uncle's new job at the bank. But they are both at the dance.

Her dark eyes and her dark hair and her darkly radiant shine. She swims in the warmth of the voices and the closeness of the bodies. Most of them feel awkward and already too hot. Not her; she loves this. She feels cool and skilful and her eyes are full of light. Her special dress and her dancing shoes. There is no stopping her and, as she moves, the centre of the dance-hall shifts with her.

He has come too. It hasn't been easy lately. He has galloped all the way holding a letter that recommends him to the Polish Bank. He didn't think it would be this hard to learn a new language, to understand another world. But he has felt silly and isolated and he misses his mother. He has learnt to press shirts and polish shoes and to keep his gaiters clean. He has also had to earn a living.

And he really doesn't know how to dance. If he knew, he would go for the dark girl with radiant eyes. He longs to be back home with his mother and sisters, and even with that stern frightening disapproving father of his, because back home he understood what was happening. Sometimes – or quite often – he didn't like it, but he knew how it was even if he didn't concentrate on it; he could dream alongside the running of real life.

In this new place the whole of his mind is consumed with survival. Nose, ears and eyes close to the ground making sure that the real stays around. His blond hair has started to get thinner at the top.

They will argue about the correct way to chop onions and cook borscht, about how to impress their guests and how a boy should be brought up. He will invoke Europe's golden rules and she will laugh in his face – a bitter and disappointed laugh: her revenge for the humiliation of having entered his dream and given it the calibre of reality, for having loved his story, for having had to defend him and his lot against her

father's wrath, for having to run away with him and
for having married him. She feels she has become the
shape of her father's broken dream.

Her father, who knows how to choose good timber
but has no appreciation for the blue in the Captain's
eye. Or the way in which the Captain makes you feel
the salt of the earth, the queen of the new world; those
dreamy eyes that crown all that dandy arrogance
– the best dressed man at the ball – the manners and
the beautiful accent, the hesitation before finding the
appropriate word, the apologetic smile for not knowing how to do the charleston; and then again, how he
holds you and stuns you with the Viennese waltz.

A man from another world with so many stories to
tell and with such certainty that you are made of magic,
that you hold all the brilliance of his future, that you
are not just another one of the pack or look like your
sister, or have to try harder, but that you are the one.
The one and only one.

There are no wedding pictures. No dress, no presents.
The tide of disapproval pushes them out of the country: they turn their shared loneliness into romance
and run away to marry. Afterwards, they have their
photo taken at the fairground: father at the wheel of

the painted aeroplane, mother sits behind him tilting her head to the camera. We stare at this picture and admire their beauty and their worldly elegance in their Panama hats. I don't think I notice that the aeroplane is made of cardboard.

I can't imagine what happens to them at this point. They must be reasonably happy because, as is often the case, the family ends up forgiving and forgetting. In the end, too much happens to have time to cry over spilt milk. There must be someone who can appreciate his charm, who can see some of his qualities and imagine a brilliant future for him. For all his contempt, one can tell how much he needs to be part of a family. And they do look good together on Saturday evenings when they dress up to go dancing. As it turns out, he can even speak a little Yiddish after all.

She wants the baby to be a boy. He waits for a girl. While she plays her game with him, making him write lists of exotic and manly and poetic names, he plays his own game in secret. He imagines a little blond and foreign princess, one to speak with him in their own private language, one that can read his thoughts and place her little hand on his troubled forehead and

soothe him and refresh him. A cool little presence
that will stand over him and allow him to forget this
hot sticky incomprehensible humid noisy unruly
damned country.

When the first girl is born La Rusita feels twice
cheated. Her sisters can understand the disappointment but cannot see why she blames him with such
conviction. But he knows that it is his fault. That
his secret dreaming has not made him a millionaire
but that it brought in the Polish baby girl, the magic
princess, the tender hand, the little made-to measure
mother, all for him alone.

La Rusita can see nothing of herself in this child.
The colours, the manner, the tone of voice are all
wrong. This is clearly the Captain's daughter (mother,
wife). A whole foreign family has landed in her house
in the small body of this alien baby.

She turns to her own. With relief, she melts into
the safety of the faces that look like her, the voices that
speak like her, the familiar smells, the borscht and the
kneidalegh as they always were before.

She says I never had a chance with mum she put me
in charge of everything she says and I did it because
it made sense to me because then I really was daddy's

little bride I could run his family for him I could do it and she could not. Every time she wasn't there I must have minded somehow but I don't really remember she says it was more that we were rid of her that we could carry on playing mothers and fathers and I thought you were my baby and I had stolen you from her she says mum left it entirely up to me to make sure you'd be looked after at weekends. She was no good at most things couldn't sew couldn't clean couldn't wash or soothe a baby or keep them asleep at night or happy during the day she had no real table manners she couldn't cook properly. Daddy said so.

That the second one is another girl is no surprise to anyone. Perhaps nobody hopes for any changes but just more and more of the same. Even she seems to know from the beginning that she belongs to no one. She cries and she screws up her little face, she won't eat; she tries everything possible to initiate a dialogue but there is no one there. And although this new baby has all her beauty, La Rusita is not fooled. She knows by now that only a boy can be truly hers. This little girl will have to manage alone as she once had to. This is what sisters are for, to keep each other out of trouble, to tell each other frightening stories and then get under the covers and huddle together all night long and argue and tell on each other and then make up. But that comes later. Now it is time for the boy.

Neither of them knows how to speak about the ice that has gathered around them. It was alright to use words to describe the world as it was waiting to be. But there is nothing to name the sharpness of the edges that keep them at a distance. I can try saying disappointment, misunderstanding, resignation, resentment, disillusion, destiny, change, impossibility, despair. But those two don't speak. They lie side by side in the matrimonial bed and wait for something to happen next. It is hot.

In the middle of the night the small house heaves. All doors are open for a breath of fresh air. Time is suspended in a truce. I know those moments so well. I knew them in my bones before I ever had the thoughts to describe them. No more nagging, sighing, whispering or turning of pages. The click of the lightswitch and a dense silence.

She still has the smooth brown body that reaches out from the eyes; he can still hold her in that tender boyish way. In a while, nobody really knows how this war began or why it goes on. The two little girls are far away now. It is still warm and easy and it melts the heart for a short time. There is a fairground, there is a dance; there was a time when all they wanted was to be together, when they were the richness of each other's lives. The mattress tells its love song while La Rusita and the Captain feel the tears on each other's faces.

It is a tragedy that these things don't last. How the intimate certainty of the dark can crack to bits with the noises of the day. We could have been happy and well adjusted. We could have bathed in the love that our parents felt for each other at times. We could have grown to make our own children happy. But there are too many problems, too many phone calls, too many jealousies and unreasonable demands.

I am not saying that things were bad all the time. That La Rusita did not have moments of tenderness and regret in which she held those two little girls close and tight and whispered sweetness in their ears. Sometimes she heard them giggle in the other room and she envied the nanny that now cared for them. It did occur to her that she would have been able to mother them better if only they hadn't been hers. If they hadn't been enmeshed into her life by looking like her and like her own mother and like her husband's mother. If only

they could have been other little girls, like her but not
of her, she would have enjoyed their brightness, their
eagerness, their longing.

Well, there is a boy now: what they both wanted. He
looks like the Captain and is rooted in her. He belongs
to both. An angel with blond curls and blue eyes, girl
and boy in one, foreign and familiar at the same time,
a homage to compromise. The Captain knows that his
mother would be proud of him if she were to hold this
little boy. He writes to her and sends a photo.

This is the time when a wound could have been
healed. He dares to think that even his father may
have been proud of him. He has a car and a shop and
a proper little family. They all go out together on
Sunday afternoons. He can say to himself that this is
what he was trying to look like, what he now is. Not
even he had imagined that this gap could close. He's
given up the gaiters but he pays for the maid who
keeps his shoes shining. Every Wednesday evening
he goes to the barber and has his head steamed and
trimmed and shaved. He talks business from mirror
to mirror and everybody smokes. His little daughters play between the leather chairs and the other men
tell him how pretty and clever they are. He patiently

waits for the day when he will bring the boy in for a haircut.

The only problem is that this is 1939. That here is another beginning of a nightmare with no end. That for all that he has managed to secure and anchor in this new life he will still have to get the letters from his mother, listen to the radio and read the news; he will have to talk to friends and the police and the Polish embassy. He will have to hear again and again that whether he knows it or not he is a Jew and so are his mother and the rest.

At first he praises his good fortune. It must have been his luck that sent him ahead of his family to make him into a hero, the true blue Captain who will gallantly rescue them and settle them into the new world. He is secretly pleased for this opportunity to be absolved from all loss. He envisages his father, now dead, finally blessing him for what he so often cursed him. This is the moment of forgiveness.

I think that he continues to feel this way long after everybody else has realized that there is no hope. When there are no more letters or news or traces, when La Rusita tells her family to stop asking, when he tries to avoid his friends and begins to lose his sleep. When he starts hitting the boy.

It was awful she says I thought I must have done something wrong it is true that I felt jealous that I hated the boy because he seemed to make everybody happy at once that we some times pinched him and scared him to make him cry. But this was only because mum and dad loved him she says. It didn't feel the same when dad started to hit him she says then I felt that something had gone wrong for ever because mum was asking me to do something to talk to him to distract him somehow and I thought I could but I couldn't I didn't make any difference to his rage or his sadness she says. He sank into the armchair in the dark and sighed and said words to himself. Mum said he's going mad we cried the boy kept running away from school and mum said I should keep my eye on him but it made no difference she says it made no difference anymore.

It is true that wars come to an end and boys grow into men and rage burns out and remorse turns into melancholy. And yet there is no end to this suffering. The punishing stops but the fear of being punished does not; no one can die again or have another go at living. Some things are irreversible.

As the war is over, the family dreams of forgetting. Like everyone else, they are swept along by relief and hope. It must be possible to bury all the pain and the confusion and the stupid mistakes. It must be possible to live alongside the dead and to rejoice in surviving. But who will dare to remember without feeling leaden? How can something new ever happen again? Is it true that people can change? Will I change? Have I suffered enough to deserve to be different? Am I allowed to desire? Can I now aspire to be?

Mother, father, two big sisters, a big brother. Among these questions, I am born.

TWO

Jorgito

Brought all the way from America. Beautiful blue eyes, blond wispy hair, nose and chin like two small pinches, those delightful sea-shell ears and the mouth, brief and profound, a mouth to get lost in, a mystery, a jewel.

I loved him immediately. I must have lost interest in the procedures, I went into a day-dream as he was handed over to me. There had been the absence, the sense of loss, the waiting, the not knowing. There had been the arrival, the celebration, the pain of having to share, the noise and the family crowd. Is this what it is like to have a baby?

I do not remember the precise moment. I mean, I do not remember looking at him or him at me because I only remember the all-enveloping sensation of holding and looking and smelling my Jorgito. Something very slightly incongruous between his soft warm body

and his cool hard head. But the matching red cap and
suit more than make up for that. I can hold him with
an arm, tightly against my chest; I can make him give a
little grunt by pressing hard on his stomach.

Once I have Jorgito I am settled. All the others
can squabble over the loot. How many packets of bub-
ble-gum each, which colour sweat-shirt, the length of
the bracelets and the size of the plimsolls. I am lost to
all that. Is it possible that this is my first one? He feels
like the only one, and how I am to know whether there
were no others or whether the others didn't count?

Jorgito comes all the way from America; my father
puts him in my arms; he chooses him for me; he brings
me a boy. I don't play dolls with Jorgito. He sleeps in
his cot in my room and I get him up and sort him out
and feed him and change him and spank him as the case
may be. He shares my life with me and we don't go out
very much. If people want to see me, they can come
and visit. Not many do.

This is me. I am looking in the mirror. The mirror covers the length of my body. I press my forehead against
hers – the one in the mirror. It is cool and very hard.
There is no way in which the two foreheads can merge
into each other. But if I roll mine sideways against the

surface of the mirror she does it too. We are so close, but it does not feel like we touch. This is me, I say. I repeat my name again and again. I look at her mouth saying what I say. I look through the mist that forms around her mouth and disappears just seconds later leaving a running tear. I see a brown eye and then another. I roll from one view to the other and make the mist with my words: this is me. This is me with the very large head. A hard large head and no body. In the almost dark sitting-room, behind the curtains, standing by the mirror.

This is my father, who sinks in the armchair every mid-day. He waits for lunch to be ready and listens to my mother's shrill voice giving commands: somebody to run to the baker's, somebody to bring the soda-bottle from the refrigerator (American), somebody to bring an extra chair from the dinning-room. My father cools down from the mid-day heat. He is a polar bear brought down to the tropics; he should have been left were he belonged; he might wilt and die in this heat. I fetch his soda-water for him. He sighs and drinks and tells me that I give him the best soda-water in town. I sit on his lap. I love him with all my heart.

These are my two big sisters. I should love them both
the same and I think I do, in the day-time, that is. But
in the night, in my bed, I know that for me they are
different. One is out there, brings friends in, argues,
makes sharp jokes and sings songs; she lets me sing
with her and I learn all the words by heart so that
I can become like her as soon as possible. She doesn't
pay much attention to the family but she cares about
the world. She is very busy making the world better.
I think that all the songs are about that. I love her clear
robust voice. When she sings, snow-flakes of stillness
land all over me; I go quiet inside and it seems as if
everything around me goes quiet too.

My other sister lives inside me. I can see that she
also has friends and looks pretty and reads books. But
her principal existence is in my head and also, sometimes, behind the curtains in the sitting-room. With
this big sister we talk mostly about me. She is very
kind and pleased about everything I do. We don't like
our parents and, if we try really hard, we don't have
any parents. Then it is just the two of us and we can
be a girl and her mother – no one else to annoy us. She
can't sing, but sometimes she tries. When she does,
some strange lost whisper comes out of her throat. My
other sister giggles but I am fascinated by the sadness

and the longing that my big sister keeps locked up in her chest. Usually I don't think about this because I am listening to the poems that roll from her mouth. Lying under the best dining table, we go over and over the words, fixing them on the rough underside of the table-top with all the power of our minds.

It is a search for meaning. When she gets into the 'I' character that unfolds within that family she risks getting cornered by a childish voice of limited scope. How could she inhabit each character and yet have the freedom to hover around and be tied to none? If the characters are too real, if the relationships are meticulously described, the story becomes linear and meaning vanishes. What she really searches for is being her self now as well as all the others that she has been before.

This family has a lot of potential: a loving father, an effective mother, two sensitive well adjusted daughters and a little girl rearing to go. But where is the boy?... There was a boy, wasn't there?

The boy is at boarding school. He's gone to the only boarding school in the land, some English folly, a boys' prison without the sentence. There's got to be a way to keep this boy under control. He steals and

cheats and kicks and spits. He breaks beautiful things,
he won't go in the bath, he makes everybody embarrassed when he shouts and punches other children in
the playground. What are we to do with a boy like that?
This is where badness has a ball. This boy will have
to go through war, concentration camp and despair all
over again. Somebody has got to do it... And how can
a family hope to choose? We wouldn't be able to go on
living if we knew that. We need not to know. We need
to puzzle over the mystery of this bad boy. When his
sisters are so clever and polite, when his father works
so hard and will spend a fortune on his education,
when his mother protects him and makes secret pacts
with him and begs him to try a little harder.

I hear the shouting sometimes. It is hard to believe
that that soft warm polar bear, that captain in blue suit,
that waltzer, is the same one that thunders and crashes
around the house, chasing after his own shadow, his
failure, his shame, his son.

  Usually Jorgito and I stay in the bedroom. We
hear the noise of traffic from the street, we look out of
the window, we go through the feeding and changing
and sleeping and visiting a hundred times over. I talk

a lot and I press Jorgito's stomach to get him to do his little grunt.

I also hit him. I take his clothes off and put him over my lap and spank his bottom again and again in a rhythmic manner that helps to soothe both of us and makes some difference to the noises coming from the house. And another thing: I have discovered that if I stick my nose between Jorgito's cold lips and then press him hard I can breathe-in the deep smell of his rubber body. I get intoxicated by the warm and stale air that passes from Jorgito to me.

This house is a train station. Everybody stops here, but only for a short while. In the morning it is mother and the maid, the smells from the kitchen and mother's busyness. She runs from the pots to the telephone, she tells the maid, she tells her friends. I listen for signs that she will go out this afternoon. Again. Every day everybody wants her and she wants them back. She visits and they all wait for her, and when she gets there she sits and stays still and talks and laughs. I long for her to sit with me, to come and visit Jorgito and me. I know that this must be true because she is my mother and I am a very small girl; but I only know it now as I see it on this page: that I desperately wanted her to sit down and be still. To stop standing on the platform and peering at a distance to see if the next train is coming yet. Where exactly does she hope to go?

The little girl is very bright – cute and bright, everybody says so. And she causes no trouble. Unlike the boy, there is no need to send her away; on the contrary, it is a pleasure to come back home and find her there, keeping herself busy with her dolls and her bits of paper. Or following the maid around the house, asking and listening and being helpful. It must have something to do with having big sisters, but one can hardly remember she is only small; she is so independent and reasonable and enchanting. She can't wait to grow up. In fact, it would be absurd to send her to nursery because she probably wouldn't play with other children. She much prefers the company of adults to all that playing nonsense. And in any case, she can already read some words.

Words words words, what is there to say? An ever decreasing circle of words going on and dying down in personal history. Another biography. So? Why this one? What has escaped her until now is that depression is not just sadness but emptiness: a most distressing sense of lacking. To have images to describe is not the same as having stories to tell. I am crazy about stories. This is why I sit there and listen and listen and listen some more. I have this one about the blind old man with his old wife who has lost her mind. He drags her around and speaks to her while his own memory fades. How do you manage without eyes and without memory and without a wife who can really be there? But he wants her right with him. He wants to feed her and wipe her and settle her; he wants her to be his aging baby. He needs her all to himself even if she has become a damaged shell. Even if she longs finally to be so helpless and so useless and so worn that there is no more service in her to give out. So that now her other life can begin, that one where she lies down and gets food in her mouth and warmth in her legs and faces in her eyes and voices in her ears that she can allow in or keep out, all of that at the drop of an eyelid. The life she thought she would never have.

But where is the boy? Although the school is like a prison, with high fences, hard and cold beds, meagre meals and whistles for voices, they say that it caters for little gentlemen. As it turns out, this is what they do in England to boys with a future. Maybe the harshness of this place is designed to throw them in together; maybe their effort to endure it is what turns them from malnourished creatures into buoyant leaders of the empire; maybe it works on them that way, but not on our boy.

At first he wants to join in. He likes the unbelievably green grass, the colourful costumes for each different game, the teachers with the funny accent. He likes being safe from his father's wrath and prefers the whistles to certain tones of voice that filled him with dread at home.

A story to tell. The story is simple: this boy does not get anywhere. He is a dead loss. He has a heart attack at thirty-five when, trying to impress people he doesn't even know, he lifts a motorbike single-handed into the back of a lorry.

I put it this way because I have to think of his life backwards in order to understand this style of truncated suicide. I can then imagine his efforts at the sports pitch, his attempts to catch up with the older boys, the way in which he would betray one tentative alliance in the face of promises of glory yet to come.

The case is that he is losing ground, that soon after the first glimmer of possibility, where his blond

hair and blue eyes slid easily into this team and that
project, he gets louder and louder and further and further removed from what might be real in him. He tells
stories of violence and honour and doesn't know he has
only dreamt them. He needs the approval of his peers
and he seeks to strike against the grain of the cold and
unbending school. The stone floor and the exposed
brick wall graze his skin every time he gets pushed or
shoved and he can't always wipe his tears before meet-
ing the mocking look of another child.

Every night he dreams he is running. He hears the
thumping of his shoes on the ground and his heart in
his chest. Sometimes he realizes he is hovering over the
road, flying just above it and going very fast; he goes so
fast that he can't see where he is but he knows that he
has left the school behind and he cries but nobody can
see him now so it doesn't matter; he is on his own now,
nobody looking or speaking about him; for as long as
he runs he will be safe.

Again, that telephone. Again it is for her. Always.
She's just been doing her nails, she keeps her fingers
wide spread with the red blades far apart. Her voice
shrills 'hello'. Now the skin of her neck fills all over
with red blotches and the corners of her mouth drop

down until the lips are only a black line; she wants to say something but they keep going at the other end. Several times she opens her mouth and starts a noise but the word-machine on the other side will not make any space. The more she hears the angrier she gets about all that noise poured in her ear. When she can finally have her turn she says you find him you bastard what kind of school are you what are we going to do with that boy.

Here's another story. I leave home. I go on a boat for three weeks. I see the black frothy sea and the blue skies gradually clouding over. I sit beside the swimming pool and play table-tennis until I freeze. I catch a cold. It is windy and grey as I have never known it before. I am in Earl's Court. I write home: 'everybody can dress as they like here, nobody looks, are you alright?' I know they are not: I know the captain is dying, but why should a child have to live through her father's death? How long should a daughter pay for her parents' guilt? Is it really me who has to makes sure that the chain breaks here? These are questions that I never ask myself. Like the boy, I am only running. My heart is thumping inside my head, I am out of breath and still going, I don't mean to stop. I like the way nobody looks at you here because I don't have to look either. I have left Jorgito with my parents.

When I return to visit I will find his soft rubber body rotting under his red dungarees. Fortunately I am now a grown-up, I understand decay and I don't really play with dolls any more.

THREE

Sunday Lunch

Chopped onions, tinned sardines. Put back inside the boiled egg whites, mashed into a paste with the yolks. Lots of vinegar in the salad dressing. Big cubes of meat stewing in the brown sauce with round slices of carrot and sticks of celery floating around. Juana the cook pricks a piece of crusty bread at the end of a long fork and pushes it deep into the stew pot. The dripping morsel emerges intact at the end of the prong, a live offering that I hold unsteadily and, having learnt from experience, I now blow to cool down. I put it close to my lip, still too hot, another blow, still smoking, a bit of patience, once again. Now. I squeeze the spongy chunk within the safe confines of my mouth, tongue pressing upwards towards the palate, lips closed tightly to avoid wasteful dribbles; all the juice, big gulps of it, warm and salty and thickened by the disintegrating bread, passing sweetly through my throat and filling my belly with softness. Why can't Sunday stay like this forever?

It takes some shouting and coercing to get them all at the table. The girls would pretend that they are busy with home work, the boy would have to get out of bed where he keeps out of the way most of the time since he is back at home. The little one seems to be the only one interested, but she gets busy in the kitchen with the maids, as if she were not part of this family. And the Captain is nowhere to be seen.

As usual, we can see in our mother's eyes that he should have been here a long time ago, that he is not to be trusted. His business extends from commercial deals with his Polish friends to buying and selling unlikely items like sets of tea-spoons or land plots up north. Or horse-betting at weekends. He tries in every possible way to keep his family afloat. He dreams. He gambles. What this man dreams of could only materialize in dreamland.

Dreamland is half-an-hour away on the bus, on the edge of the city. With a bird's eye, one could see the suits and the manly hats converging towards the oval structure, walking or floating towards their destiny, driven by hope and pride and their special tips.

It is after the war, when the country enlarges and deepens, receiving the damaged and the damned, and turning their despair into promise. Some build their future empires, some peddle on others' need, some have lost all sense of reality and expect – demand – some retribution for their losses. They wear felt hats in the winter and Panamas in the summer, protecting themselves from the harsh blue sky, and sharpening their view as they follow the race through their binoculars. They form a secret fraternity because they know that their hope is brittle: it goes to pieces every Sunday afternoon. Only in the outmost isolation – laboratory conditions – it is possible to foster it and build it up again during the next six days, to tell oneself that a small mistake happened, or that God needed to attend to someone else first, and be ready to return to the racecourse the following Sunday in full form, boasting with a sense of specialness and anticipation, as if about to enter into a love embrace for the first time.

He is a poker player too, and this is the skill he deploys as he steps back into his house. He carries fresh strawberries in the summer and roast suckling pig in the winter. Always something delicious that goes to my head through the nose. To us he is the bearer of good

things, but mother searches inside his yellow eyes, sees
the change of shade on his skin, precisely at the level of
his shirt collar and on the topside of his hands; perhaps
later she will delve in his pockets or she will ask for
some more money for the weekly shopping so as to
ascertain the size of the catastrophe to be revealed.

But for now we all sit at the table and start to eat.
This picture is confused. I do not miss him on Sunday mornings, even though I know that he is not there.
But if he has gone to the races before lunch, where is
he then on Sunday afternoons, when the loneliness
really begins?

The meal is over, big sisters and brother have better
things to do elsewhere, father not there and mother
having a siesta. It is downhill from here to Monday
morning. And even if I haven't yet experienced all that
many Sundays – or not as many as I know now there
are still to come – I already know that there is nothing
but white dullness stretching ahead, I am on my own
with my napping mother; nothing will rescue me from
this death, from this void, from this blank. She might
never wake up, she might allow everything to go dark
and even more still while she lies on her bed, some-

times turning, sometimes coughing, fallen into the bottom of a precipice where she is happy to remain.

I should have never allowed it to happen. It was a folly and a madness. I let him persuade me when I had plenty of evidence that I am not cut out for this. Three children, three abortions and yet I still listen to his plea: that it would be different now, that the war was nearly over, that we had the means, that we were getting older.

I know that I am not cut out to be a mother. I don't really like babies, or even children. There have been already too many in my life. And I know that it is not really her fault but I can't help it. I want to be alone, I want to curl up and close off. Or go away and never come back. Or fall for a dark stranger and disappear into the distance. I want out.

When I watch her in the kitchen with Juana my heart stops for a moment. I can see that she is small, lonely, waiting for me to mother her. She wants to be part of what is happening, she wants to be thought about. I can see that she is not asking for much, and yet it is more than I ever had. I see her following Juana about and chattering to her, watching what she does in a way she has never watched me. But what do I do anyway that a child could make sense of?

Juana is a smart woman. She loves that child but she knows her place, so she keeps her distance. She doesn't hug her or touch her very much but she holds her with her talk and with the little special things that she gives her: a slice of carrot, a mouthful of bread dripping with meat juice. She feeds her like a mother hen; she can see that this child is a little chick with a wide open beak and I am a hawk, waiting behind the scenes and ready to snatch and drop her should my position be challenged.

From here I can hear my fourth child tip-toeing around the house. She is trying to be quiet and she is also trying to wake me up. She longs for me and she fears me at the same time. And although I know exactly what it is like to feel like that about your mother, I still cannot get out of bed and hold her.

FOUR

First Day at School

She said my birthday is coming up in June. I thought it would be nice to have the party with all the other girls. Loads of presents because there are loads and loads of little girls here, each one perched on their bench, all looking so pretty with their plaits and pony tails and some have fringes like I want to have... Maybe in June, when I have my birthday... All the girls look a bit like the teacher, standing at the front of the class, talking to my mother above me. They look at each other and speak quietly. I am standing right next to my mother's leg, feeling the warmth of her skin on my arm, it comes from her leg through her cotton dress; still very hot, and it is only after breakfast. The girls look like the teacher and they all look like birds on top of their perches, pigeons in their white coats, with all the starch of Monday mornings, pleated at the front, your mother holds it in front of you and you slide your hands into the scratchy arms of the delantal, then you turn round for your mother to do the buttons up, all the way to the collar which feels too tight around the neck, never mind, you think when you are older, because as soon as you have kissed her good-bye you will unbutton that last one at the collar and if somebody tells you off later you will go: 'Who, Miss? Me, Miss? I didn't notice it was undone'.

But this is year one and all the girls look like white birds in rows, with their bows tied at the back, those knotty bulges that hurt when you lean back on your wooden seat, some so beautifully made by mothers with thin agile fingers that can make the bow look as if it is about to start flapping and take off with the little girl cradling inside it.

So my mother says that yes, that she has thought of that but she thinks nursery is a waste of time and I am about to have my birthday anyway and I feel a burning on the crown of my head but cannot look up because some of the girls are already looking my way and I have to see inside their eyes before I am told to go and sit at that bench, my own bench! right at the end of one of the four long rows. I feel my mother's hand on the back of my shoulder, she is pointing me towards my place and pushing me away at the same time, I hold on to the temperature of her palm on my back, even when I am already half-way through the corridor of starchy seagulls, with their beaks towards me, screeching in my direction: 'What's your name? How old are you? Can you play the hop-scotch?'

I feel the lump in my throat and concentrate on not falling down, not turning back, not letting myself shout or run or lash out. I smile and nod once or twice and when I finally turn to wriggle into my seat I see no mother at the front.

I can hear the echo of my steps down the corridor. I can tell that I am walking too fast. Nobody else seems to be moving around in this building and I know that it would be better if I slowed down. But I won't, I can't. I am scared that I will hear her calling, that the teacher might change her mind and say that she really is too young after all, that we should wait another year. Do teachers know what it is like to reach this point? To finally let go of the last, the fourth child, the one that was never meant to be? To find yourself a mother and stay that way for fifteen years?... What happened to me? I was never going to be my mother, I was never going to shuffle my feet around a husband and let him have me on the creaky bed while I made lists in my mind to make sure that everybody got fed, clothed, schooled, vaccinated, aired and ironed. I was another generation, feisty to choose my own husband, to go to University, to earn my living, even to be on my own all my life if I had to. I was nobody's woman. So I hated my heart when it jumped at the sight of his suit, and hated my head when it spun at the smell of his perfume and hated my skin when it glowed at the touch of his arm. Because I could already see that my toes would root to the ground and my arms would branch and my trunk would expand and hollow. I know that I shouldn't be running along the empty corridor of my youngest daughter's new school, but I am longing to come into the light, the noises of the street. I am shaking off the soil on my feet as I run and by the time I reach the gate I will probably be hovering three inches above the ground. I will throw myself against the crowds and disappear in their mist. No woman, no daughter, no mother, no trace.

FIVE

Jewish Prince

She has to marry in flat shoes because he is shorter than she is. She has to marry now because he is all alone after his parents' accident. She has to marry because he wants to take her away; because father would be mad if I don't get married – mad, sad, starving, dead: everybody gets married in the end.

Those two surely love each other. I only need to have a look at them together and I feel as if I were on a cloud myself. They walk hand in hand pulling and push-ing and giggling because it is exciting to feel so close and to be at the centre of everyone's dreams. And I don't know how they manage this – but I never feel excluded: I seem to always be part of what is going on between them. I am the ready-made baby of this pre-tend baby-couple. And we all love this game. He is a

Jewish prince: nose and glasses, wiry hair and a sharp
mind full of twists and humorous curls; an only child
and – even more – he is going to be a doctor! He snug-
gles into our family with the confidence of someone
who has been long awaited. We have all been waiting
long for someone, and it is my big sister who brings
along the young messiah and, when he looks upon
us, we are all redeemed. We all shine in the mirror of
his eye.

I am crazy about him. Follow him around like a
shadow, even if I am sitting in a different room from
him. I want his look. I want the way he speaks to me
taking for granted my understanding, as if my mind
is infinitely expandable, as if there is nothing I cannot
grasp. I develop this thirst, I want to drink and drink,
pour the water all over my face, my hair, my body.
I want to laugh until I die. This man is mine.

Another woman's man. They are the best. They look
at you but they make no demand. They are all longing, and promise, and unspoken understanding. They
raise the hair of your nape by touching you with their
eye. They must have blue eyes. We dance. It is dark
and damp and I know the shape of my body as it rubs
against the hard parts of his. That old exciting demon

behind those sweet and vague blue eyes. He's got a
sports car and loads of money, he's got two children
and he's got his own woman waiting in his bed. And
yet when he curves his body around mine I possess the
whole adult world to toy with at my leisure. I do not
understanding his folly. Why me? He does not seem
like a dreamer or a supplicant, and yet he offers his
adult self for me to despise. I love to get my revenge on
him; I am truly excited.

Theirs will have to be a long romance because they are
only eighteen. And these are the best years of my life
– happening in someone else's life. For the first time
I feel that I have a proper mother and father and a
proper family. I am cherished, I have a place. Could
this possibly be true? It makes me sad. It worries me
about my future. Have I already reached the peak of
my story? Will there be life after this romance – their
romance? Will I ever fall in love again?

My sisters go to University; my brother struggles at
school. I've been to summer camp with my cousin. We
were glad we could hold hands when the coach took us
away with our rucksacks, our packed sandwiches and
a whole crowd of anonymous children. But I have no

other memory of her for the rest of that holiday. This is
the time when I discover friendship. I am in a tent with
four other girls. We move as a block during the day and
in the night we whisper in the dark from our camp-
beds. I love them because they are in my tent. I have
no idea of their past or their circumstances, whether
they were there with each other before I came along or
if they felt like me, frightened of feeling lonely when
they arrived. We are left to huddle together, and we
rejoice in it for the next few years. It is only much later
that we really learn each other. There are boys too.
They thread the fabric of our talk. We discuss them,
report on them, speculate, compare and dismiss them.
Sometimes one of us has a boyfriend. The group wob-
bles and staggers at the impact of this disruption, but
in the end it proceeds on. Other girls are not allowed,
but boys can pirouette around us and oil the wheels
of our cart.

Later on my cousin and I are at the funfair, having a
go on the big wheel. It takes for ever to load all the people onto their seats. We go higher and higher talking
through the screams, the music below and the wind
above. She tells me that she is in love with the summer camp director. She speaks about this love with

sorrow because she knows it is impossible, and I listen in silence and fascination. I know that I too could be feeling like her, but I don't. I refuse to think that my love is also impossible. Because they are getting married – I suppose I think. But who? Who will I marry when they do? I am too old to marry my doll; my father is too old to marry me, and my brother has already begun to haunt me. I am waiting for a tragic moment but I don't know it. For now, there is still time.

Peeping in and out of my story. The story is inside the page waiting to be drawn out. Do I want it? Can I stop it? I could certainly stop it. I could let it stay secret until I die - nothing easier than that. I could let life live itself with no thought, paint the mirrors black, close the distance and be at one with – pasted upon – myself; I could turn off the characters and let old dogs lie. Why continue and pretend to know, or to want to know? We will only get hurt.

They have me as their joint project. They delight in delighting me, intriguing and surprising me – and life feels like a playground. Love is contagious and I catch it. I thrive in the multiplicity and richness of my ever enlarging family. I listen to all stories, all sides, all

plots. I pass from knee to knee, mesmerized by conversation, descriptions of the Universe, ad hoc drawing
lessons, picture-books on comrade Stalin, Western
movies. It is as if the whole world is now throbbing
within our home. I have no memory of my parents at
this point; they recede into the background and lose all
importance. Aged seven or eight, I am going through
my first adolescence and nobody appears to dispute
it – it seems to suit all. My parents can skip over the
complications of having this late child extending the
burden of their responsibilities until the end of their
lives; my sisters can play mothers and fathers with the
benefit of always being on the good-guy side; I can
work hard to fit around all these different versions of
parental constellations; I love each one of my puta-
tive parents and I am fully aware of my task: being the
dream child.

It gets harder at night. The midnight spell breaks at
about eight o'clock when I report back home and my
parents become my parents. The dark landing, the
corridor, the front door. Do I have my own key? The
maid lets me in – she is making my dinner. Parents
out, sisters out, brother was never in. The lighting of
this scene is always a fluorescent white tube stuck to

the high ceiling, never quite bright, always flickering slightly. No sound except the radio from the kitchen and whatever else I might manage to manufacture by myself in the silence of the empty apartment. I sit, I walk about, I tiptoe along the corridor, I sit, I wait.

I find my food on the table – a table set for one. I sit I smell I taste. I fear. I am scared of the silence and the dark and the loneliness that comes next. I chew on the piece of steak but I know I will not swallow it. I collect all the grey mashed fibre in a ball between my teeth and the inner wall of my cheek, and then I chew some more. Eventually, I spit it on the plate. The maid is disgusted but she wants to go. She sweeps the whole show away and tells me she is off now.

I knew this already. Time has stopped.

All I remember is the window into the night; the street-lights and the cars making shadows on the ceiling of my bedroom. Occasionally, the whole building trembles as the tram goes by. I also remember my son's fear, his small body covered in sweat, his light steps on the stairs and the door of my now master bedroom opening slowly, so slowly; then his whisper, his hope to speak to me without waking me up. My fear his own. Paralysed I wait for time to move on again.

Sometimes I get to hear my mother's voice approaching from the street. Perhaps by the time they step into the flat I am already asleep. But the best is when from my bed I can see the slivers of light around the door, hear their voices and their bodies shuffling against the furniture and the walls, let their whispers sing for me and ease my fall into darkness.

There is morning tomorrow. It is only at night that I know in my bones what I do not want to know any-where else yet. Only then do I perceive the full taste of my loneliness. They are all couples, they are made for each other – I have seen it in their bodies. I have felt the purring of their desire as if walking into a magnetic field. And I am on my own: one of a kind. No sister, no man, no mother or father.

This is not my wedding and I am not the true princess.

SIX

The Twin

She stands leaning against the square column of the
front entrance. As on every day, she has come here
driven by boredom; she is longing to be with someone. She is still young enough to do what she needs
to do. Like dogs and plants, she is before she thinks.
Her loneliness moves her but she does not know it. She
is leaning against the cold black marble of the front
entrance to the apartments. The caretaker is not there
today. Pity. She likes his voice and his bushy eyebrows.
He tells the occasional story, but mostly he leans there
too, and they both watch the world go by. Now and
then he looks at her, possibly after seeing something or
someone unusual, and this is when he raises the bushy
eyebrows. Often she has no idea of what has caused the
cracking on his worn handsome face, but she knows
for certain that he is speaking to her and she likes that

– to be leaning against the black marble column, facing
him and watching the world go by. But he is not there
today, whatever day this may be. So she is alone with
the business of the street. She has to look at each face
all by herself. No one must pass unseen. If they do, she
will have to bear never ever knowing those eyes, that
mouth, the colour of that face; that face will not be in
her mind, that bit of herself will now be lost for ever.
This is why sometimes she runs behind a missed face,
rushing through the moving bodies in the road until
she is well ahead and ready to turn around and have a
good look: – ah... so this is the face she nearly missed!
And although she thought she knew what to expect
in front of that dark, thick, heavy mass of hair, those
narrow shoulders, that jumpy walk, the face is always
unexpected. So many faces; no face the same, not one
the one. No one at home. It gets dark early now and it
is sad all alone in the flat.

   Not that it is not sad here, but it is a different sort
of sadness. To be lonely in the middle of this passing
crowd is disconcerting, distracting, even entertaining.
To be lonely at home is silent and dark. So she leans
against the black marble, letting her fingers make
damp prints on the shiny surface; she makes a perfect
engraving that shrinks and vanishes in front of her very

eyes and can be made again, like the faces in the crowd, never the same one, grasped and forgotten almost at the same time.

Many years later, again all alone in the crowd. Waiting, again. Scanning the faces, looking for those who are now familiar and safe but they are not there – not there. So many faces, another hemisphere, another continent, another prototype of familiarity and anonymity. Several people are sitting on the plush carpet of the theatre hall, making a mute protest against the ways of civilization or the scarcity of chairs, or against being made to wait until the last minute for returned tickets. But they are young and clean and lively – only pretending to be tired.

The man who really is tired has waited too long to sit down. He is now sprawled on the plush carpet and he moans. We think he is drunk. We want to ignore him or despise him because tonight is our special treat. A few people are gathering around, mainly to satisfy their curiosity or perhaps to confirm that they should not worry too much about him. Next time we look he has some efficient looking characters around him and has been laid on his side. Some uniforms nearby, surely everything is now under control and we can go and see the play. There are now hundreds of otherwise engaged people around this man who has stopped moaning. We surely cannot all stop our business just because he looks white and still. On the contrary, there is a shared agreement that he should not be allowed to disturb our special evening. That we have all struggled to get here and have made an effort not to fall ill or faint or get drunk or burst into tears and ruin such a special occasion. So why should we let it be spoilt by someone else? We all have our sorrows and frailties, our future deaths. We are all alone in the crowd. His is a face that I will not see; I have accepted these things by now.

Opposite her, on the caretaker's side, the marble glares each time the lights of a passing car shine on it. It is over her reflection on the black marble that the twin becomes alive. She lends him her own face and her own voice – he becomes her companion.

But why not? – she argues. Why couldn't I have my own twin? And nobody argues back. Even though he will not come into the flat and be part of the family, he is always prepared to stand with her at the front door. If the caretaker is at his post, the twins have to take turns there; and if there is room for both of them,

they hardly ever need to run after people because of
a missing face. Whoever they might miss, they still
have each other; they can be two together; talk about
parents and wonder when theirs will be back; say that
it is getting late, or that it is getting colder, or that it
seems always to be night in the winter. She thinks to
herself that her twin has reasons of his own for wanting to be there with her. Perhaps he saw her from far
away and has dreamt of her in his little bed in the dark.
Or he knows that she is good at hopscotch. He too is
the youngest but he is a little bit taller and he is very
strong. It is better to be a boy.

It's not fair, they often say at once. They can both
open their mouths wide and make a real riot saying
just that. Not fair, not fair. As they shout it, all sorts
of really unfair things come to land around them. Having a big brother who is a bully, being born into the
family so late, not being one of her big sisters, not
having her dad to herself, everybody always being
somewhere else.

Sometimes it even seems as if her twin shouts
louder than she does. He goes red in the face and he
cries with rage. It wasn't me – she could tell the caretaker if he were around. She wouldn't make such a
racket because she can look at the clock in the shop

across the street. The clock ticks away towards the
time she will see her father's silhouette turning the
corner and walking towards her. She can recognize
his rounded shoulders under the coat, his trilby hat
and his slow walk, carrying a loaf of rye bread and
perhaps pastrami and gherkins for dinner. The taste
of company.

Again, again, again. She has come from far away
especially to see him. His heart giving way, he lies in
the hospital bed and his eyes tell her how delighted he
is to see her there. And how frightened he is that she
has come. It means the end – she would not be there if
it were not. She wishes that she could be his twin, make
him feel safe rather than alarmed by her presence. She
too is alarmed to see how small his face is now. They
both try to be casual. They do not open their mouths
wide and shout, wailing that it is not fair. Not fair. She
waits, she holds his hand, she looks into him when his
eyes let her in. She also lies. Talks about the future,
about the present, as if it mattered. He lies too: he gets
a little better. He sips some tea, he gets a bit of colour
in his cheeks. He says he'll come to the theatre and
she buys the best seats. The family mobilizes around

this small miracle: the car, the clothes, the pick up arrangements. They sit side by side to the music.

'If I were a rich man, doobby doobby doobby doobby doobby doobby doobby doo'... They survive his pauses, his pale vacillations, the sweat on his exhausted forehead. The following day she goes back. She promises. Next day he is in bed again.

'Did not suffer', says the telegram.

SEVEN

First Job

The opportunity came along unexpectedly: somebody who knew somebody said they were looking for someone – so she phoned and went along. The address was already telling, right on the elegant North Square, overlooking the green slopes. Heavy wooden gates led to a large cobbled patio; once inside, wooden floors and wooden panels on the hall – darkly perfumed wood: smell of wealth. Led into the waiting area, she sank into the armchair, staring at the wide twisting banister.

'Mr Morris will be over in a minute'. It took longer than a minute. Long enough to plug back into a certain feeling of humility and resentment about her predicament: once again she was stranded in an impossible situation. True, she had got her place at University – but this had only been what everyone expected of her. She had known before applying that her father would not have settled for less, and that the question of money would not be mentioned. As usual, money could only be considered in terms of its absence; not enough money to buy a bus pass or a warm coat once winter started. And even if it were never mentioned, she already knew the expectation had been doubled in an all too familiar way: she was to get a place at University alongside the job that would keep her whilst studying.

She heard him whistle before she saw him, a mischievous whistle tuned to no particular melody, more like a way of walking than a song. Mr Morris introduced himself while he shook her hand and led her up the stairs, giving her plenty of opportunity to admire the back of his slim hips underneath the dark blazer and to notice his narrow ankles in the fresh black shoes and to appreciate the fragrance he left behind him at each step of the long way up. By the time they reached the large office bathed in light she was smitten.

Other partners came and went, she answered all their questions and saw them glance at each other when she said how old she was – only just seventeen. In a way, she no longer felt that she cared whether they took her in or not. She had abandoned herself to her fate. Her legs had gone weak, her head was swimming, she was floating in the arms of a lover. She had already seen in his eyes that he believed that she belonged there, and that was all that mattered.

The partners seemed to be struggling with the question of her age. Would it be good or bad to put such youth at the reception desk of their smart law firm? Not to speak of the fact that she had no secretarial skills whatsoever, or any training in hanging around trying to please everybody. Was it there and then or was it later that she heard, as if from far away, that yes, that they would take her on and pay her a plentiful salary to go with the house, the staircase, the wooden panels and Mr Morris's fragrance?

She did not notice until much later that there were no windows in the reception area, that visitors laboured up the beautiful staircase to arrive at the view of her legs crossed under the pretty desk, all on her own in this dark and intimidating landing where she briefly ruled as to who should be led into the bright offices of the young lords and who should be made to sit and wait on the leather chairs by the lamp, from where they could talk to her or watch her go about the filing, the switch-boarding, the letter-opening and all the mesmerizing tasks of another day at the office.

Beautiful Mr Morris was first to arrive every morning
– not surprisingly since he only lived two hundred
yards away. This was their private time when he called
her into his large study with the magnificent windows
and they talked about the tasks of the day as if they
were planning a romantic date. He dazzled her with a
delicate mixture of subtle gossip, shared secrets and
appropriateness. It gradually became clear to her that
it was at these private moments – and only then – that
he called her Ana. The rest of the time she was Miss D,
to him and to all the other partners who rolled into the
building every day.

Mr K liked noise: he arrived with puffy eyes at
ten thirty, looking as if he might still smell of alco-
hol and women from the previous night. Mr O came
at mid-day, straight from the morning courts, as if he
had never been to bed in his life, impatient and efficient – the only partner who was still waiting for her
to get her short-hand proficiency certificate. Senator
T came now and then, usually late in the afternoons, a
tired man from the provinces, probably the most pres-
tigious trophy of this law firm's gallery, and yet always
seemingly bewildered at the ways of the urban world
and at his own affluent partners; he missed his family

and enjoyed a chat, and was actually curious about her, her opinions, her plans.

In different ways she loved them all and they all loved her. Alongside their wives, lovers, sisters and mothers, she had acquired a place in the lives of these men. In this luxurious playground where they devoted themselves to manly games, there needed to be a woman to remind them of some of the more tedious aspects of their existence. The idea of woman could be kept alive by one young girl sitting at the reception desk, evoking all women, packaging their desire within one feminine place, and safely away from each other.

This concentration of feeling upon her kept her own passion for them alive and – in this respect – she loved the whole tribe as if they were a single man; she loved them all in one and she loved to be the one woman allowed into their all male universe. In them she also loved her own father with his inaccessible world and yes, of course, she also loved her power to despise and subjugate and secretly humiliate all fathers and brothers and lovers of this world. In these opaque waters she swam, while she made their phone calls, fetched their cups of coffee, filed their documents and announced their visitors. All day, every day.

But this is not a harmless game. In time Miss Ana
D, mascot and victim, does become a real reception-
ist. After some months she allows her curiosity to lead
her to Mr K's bachelor flat where she watches him take
off his clothes and hers and become a fumbling child
against her body, proceed to do what is expected, and
get back to his usual chatter whilst kicking his legs up
in the air to the beat of his own voice, delighted with
himself, perhaps triumphant for having managed to
get in there first – being the junior partner, after all!
This event makes no difference to their work together
because, in a way, it is part of their work. If anything,
it makes Mr K a little less aggressive and noisy in the
mornings, and Ana is glad of this. And the knowledge
that this man waves his legs in the air after having sex
with his secretary stays in her mind like a secret joke,
amusing her as if someone else – someone who was
actually there – had told her about it.

Office Christmas party. Hot, humid, torrid. The party
is at Mr Morris's country home. Lavish food, velvet
lights. There are other women. In fact, these other
women have been around from the beginning but they
have always seemed remote to Ana; two typists who
adore Mr O and who surely know how to take short-

hand dictation! The disregard is mutual: to them, Ana is a dolly, a pretty face, an ornament, a male folly, a passing fancy; to Ana, they are true career secretaries, trained to assist and obey and admire, to do a similar job to hers but – she argues with herself – for other reasons. Days and weeks go by without a word passing between them.

There are also plenty of men at the party, all sitting together eating, drinking, laughing, bantering and teasing. It makes Ana feel very young and very female. There is no place to go to keep boredom at bay. So she imagines that Mr Morris knows how she is feeling; she imagines that he is looking at her and her alone – even if he appears to concentrate on being a good host and laughing at jokes and offering more food and taking care of everything and everybody. She imagines that he and she are alike, that they are both here for other reasons. She imagines that he wants her to sit next to him at the table so that they can let their arms touch very lightly and feel their legs rubbing together when they shift in their seats. She imagines that this light touch lingers on longer each time until it becomes impossible to pull away from his moist hot skin.

On the table the men are playing cards now, a little more drunk, a little more blurred, a little more tired.

Under the table, her leg is fiercely intertwined with his, rubbing and pressing and hooking, making up for the long long wait.

Did I say that Mr Morris was married and had two children? Well, he is and he has. It is difficult to explain why it is that this does not matter, why Ana does not for one moment feel hard done by. Perhaps she does not think of this as her real life yet, or perhaps she knows that the feelings she receives are real even if they remain within the boundaries of this make-believe men's world. Perhaps she herself feels like a conquering warrior: one by one skinning the scalps of her victims to hang them from her belt.

After the party Mr Morris courts her. He glances at her, whispers sweet nothings, looks for opportunities to brush against her or give her a furtive embrace. He makes a point of sighing just before he takes another call from his wife. Like a true courtier, he seems to know how to promote a sense of delicious complicity. There is never a promise or an apology, just a suspension of reality which, diluted by boredom, eases the job into the centre of Ana's life. University seems a long way away and so do mother and father and friends. Ana has disappeared into the centre of Miss D., imprisoned

in the mansion, locked in with the beast, immobilized
by the reflection of her own sleeping beauty in the
looking glass.

At last Mr Morris – her chain and her champion
– makes a move. He has sent his family to the coun-
tryside and issued an invitation: a secret first date, a
break out of prison. They are both excited. More complicity and more whispering and secret glances. All is
set. They both arrive on time; he, a little more so – as
is appropriate. She sits in his car and lets him lead the
way into the night. He parks. The trip has been short;
the site, vaguely familiar. Not a club, not a restaurant
or the promenade by the river, but a darkly lit street
and – oh god not that! – Mr K's bachelor apartment.
It is hard to tell whose trump card this really is – and
whether to call it sinister or grotesque – but it brings
Ana back to herself.

Mr Morris, more of a gentleman than a beast, gra-
ciously accepts her refusal. They go for a drink, they
listen to music, they dance a little; he keeps a modest
reserve, perhaps not wanting to be seen and recognized.
Later, he takes her home and they kiss good-night.

This last kiss breaks the spell. Finally, the smell of
coffee makes her sick and the clicking of the intercom

gets on her nerves; when she is asked to fetch another file, she cannot even begin to look for it. Senator T wants to know why she looks cross and bitter all the time; even junior partner Mr K asks if there is something the matter. But Ana leaves the job before finding the words to explain.

EIGHT

Outsider

It is dark and it is damp and it is smelly. And yet when I look outside the window it seems as if everybody else is coping. Everybody else is in the light, going somewhere, keeping busy, avoiding the cars, walking past each other, stuffing their faces with food. Busy, busy, busy. But for me each day is too long, too damn wet.

In this place everybody goes out in the rain. They take umbrellas, they take hats, or they take nothing at all and they just get wet. They get their shoes wet, their socks and their feet wet. They walk in the slush and think nothing of it. Do they go home and change all the time or do they let moss grow in between their toes? And exactly how many pairs of shoes are you supposed to have in order to keep up with this country? And if you change them, if you cannot stand your wet feet any more – say that you wash your socks in the basin of your bed-sitter, that you happen to have the right change and put your coin in the slot and get the water hot and you soap and you rinse your socks and get them all soft and sweet smelling again – where then, where, do you hang them to dry? No sooner do you hang them on the back of a chair than the water starts gathering at the toes and it begins to leak on the carpet. More dampness and – in any case – no dry socks. They will be there for ever, or long enough to get that damp smell again before they are dry. And this is just what happens with a pair of socks. We haven't even begun to worry about a shirt or a pair of pyjamas.

I know it is winter now because it is the middle of November in the calendar. 'Spring's bursting', said my friend in her letter from home; but it could have been July here as far as I am concerned and I would still not manage to get my socks dry. Not in this room at any rate. Not in this damn damp country.

I suppose I will have to face that laundry place again. As if once was not enough...

I had seen it several times from the bus. Another place full of electric light and people bustling around, everybody busy and looking as if they knew what they were doing. The first time I passed it on the bus

I wondered what it was. Not a cafe, not a pub, not a language school – what then? I looked it up in the dictionary once I managed to read the sign on it the second time round: Launderette, but it wasn't there. I did find laundry though. I guess it is a small one of those, even though it looked pretty big to me, and steamy. So this is what they do over here – I thought. None of this slaving over the basin and putting your pennies in the meter. You go to this launderette and have it all over and done with a single stroke. I told Juan about it. He was impressed. He had also noticed that corner with people coming and going and children looking bored inside. Once we worked it out we thought we would have a go at it, but we kept postponing it. Yet another thing to make sense of, like Indian curries that burn your mouth until you cry, or people that call you dear when they don't even know you... Who knows what we would have to deal with at the launderette.

Well, I know now. I went on my own because Juan was in bed, having one of those stay-in-bed-all-day days. Too cold, too foreign, too frightening to try anything else. One of those days like every other day when you think what on earth am I doing here? Anyway, I thought I had to tackle the dirty clothes problem,

I thought I had to get a move on. I suppose I also thought that I might get to talk to someone there, make friends perhaps. So I went. I told Juan I was going to go. I said: 'I am going to that laundry place and you better get ready, because I am going to come back with all the damn clothes soaking and we will need to hang them somewhere to dry. So get out of that bed and make yourself useful and put a line somewhere because I can tell you we are going to need it for the next three days'. So I put everything in the suitcase and went, feeling quite good about myself. At least it wasn't raining and that made a change.

I opened the door and the first thing that hit me was the smell. I hadn't expected that. After all, it is supposed to be a washing place, a place where things get clean and where clean people come to do their business. But it did have this indescribable smell of damp (again) and worn, mixed with old soap. I wanted to turn round and go but I thought of Juan, perhaps out of bed and hanging a line, or maybe still in bed doing nothing whatsoever. Either way I couldn't bear to go back. So I stuck it out.

I asked for the lady in charge and I immedi- ately got the looks. What lady? No laundry lady or a

bloody soul to explain how it goes. So that was what
the 'erette' was about. It means 'you are on your
own'. So I went to one of these massive round doors
and did what the other women were doing: I emptied
the suitcase inside the drum. 'That wasn't too bad',
I said to myself, 'Good to be rid of that lot. What's
next?' As if she heard my thoughts, this woman
said: 'you get the soap from that machine, dear'.
I knew by now that dear doesn't mean she knows me,
or even that she likes me, although she must have
liked me a little bit to give me a hand like that. So
I stood in the queue for the soap and I got my purse
in my hand because everybody else was doing that.
I felt encouraged. So far so good. People seemed to get
their soap and take it to the washing machine and then
they switched it on. Not that different from home, but
everybody is doing it together. Not a bad idea in a way.
Like living in a commune or in a kibbutz. Why be all
on your own at home doing these boring things when
you can be social about them? I felt positively closer to
everybody, I felt part of something – a little bit elated.

Then my turn came. I looked at the metal slot. It
had a bit of paper stuck above with a one shilling sign.
I quickly rummaged in my purse – people waiting
behind. Found a shilling and put it in; I heard nothing

and then the machine made a reassuring noise. I am on top of this, I thought, or maybe just half thought, as soap powder exploded down in all directions.

What's wrong with this machine? The queue behind me, my dirty clothes in the drum, what am I supposed to do? Go on my knees and try to scoop all the powder from the floor into the drum? I can see now why this place smells of soap and mess. I can't stand it. I am not going to get into this. It doesn't matter if it costs another shilling. I will put it in quickly and have a proper pack of soap, not all that loose stuff on the floor. So I did. And what did I get? Another explosion of powder all over the place. By now a few people were coughing and somebody had passed down an empty paper cup and put it at the receiving end of the soap dispenser. I hate this country, I hate Europe, I hate everybody.

But I did have another shilling in my purse and this time the soap fell neatly into the cup. I think the queue must have felt relieved, but they gave me the English phlegmatic treatment: nobody appeared to notice, nobody spoke, nobody looked at me as I walked, cup in hand, to my washing machine.

To find out much later that some clothes had shrunk to half their size in the tumble drier was a minor inconvenience compared with the first part of the story. At least nobody saw me when I discovered that. And I did have a moment of glory when I arrived back in the bedsit, found Juan tying a cord around a nail and said: 'Don't bother, it is all done! They think of everything in these launderettes'.

So I guess it wasn't that bad after all. But it did take it out of me. Luckily the bed was still warm so I could take off my coat and get in, and stay there for the rest of the day. Which is not very long around here because it gets dark by four o'clock – that is supposing that it was ever light before.

By now our clothes are ready to wash again, but I guess that would have happened wherever we were. Some problems you take with you no matter what country you go to.

NINE

The Piano

He had wanted to leave one on top of each desk. After one year of yielding to the principles of deferred gratification, one year of nine-to-five imprisonment, one year of trendy dressing, picking up the phone when it rang, letting your wife choose your clothes, calling her your 'wife', opening a bank account and saving every penny, after one year of slavery they did their sums and they thought they were ready – or as ready as they would ever manage to be.

In any case, the house was now falling apart. There had been police coming at five o'clock in the morning looking for drugs, there had been the theft of Juan's pocket-watch and of Simon's money. There had been Inge boiling her knickers in the puchero pot – the only large one they had managed to own, specially bought to make chicken soup as they remembered it from home: a boiling aromatic memory of mothers and families, all utterly spoilt by one Scandinavian woman with lice in her pants. They did not feel they could ever recover from that assault, plus Paul tearing the living room apart one middle-of-the-night night when he thought about his messed up life, the arid desert that appeared in his mind when he thought of home, the infinite moments he had spent locked up in prison. As the crushing noises and his sobs filled up the house, Juan left the warmth of their bed and went downstairs to sit with him, shaking from cold and from uncertainty whilst Paul continued to smash and cry his way through any furniture and crockery that was still left. Once it was all done, the two of them cleared up and embraced at the bottom of the stairs. Paul slept like a baby and Ana heard Juan shouting in his dreams. The following morning they counted their money.

Paul's outburst did it. The landlord had been trying to ignore the continuous traffic of unspecified visitors, the teenagers coming in when they should have been at school, the long-haired sandalled dreamers, men with earrings, women with multicolour babies, the lights in the sitting room always on, and the house steaming with music and smoke. But that morning they got

their notice: one month to pack up and go. The neigh-
bourhood should have been glad to see the back of so
many old vans, squeaky bikes and motorcycle parts.
Some in the house were relieved to be told to disband,
some were angry and affronted, some felt desolate at
the prospect of becoming homeless again. For Juan
and Ana it was the signal. The world was opening up
again, mysterious, frightening and alluring. So Juan
prepared the flyers:

> *Blackbird singing in the dead of night*
> *Spread your open wings and learn to fly*
> *All your life you've been only waiting*
> *For this moment to arrive.*

He counted the desks in each room of each floor of
the large building in the City where he worked; he
rehearsed his resignation speech on the bus and pic-
tured the morning after his final departure. He plotted
a way in which, on that day, he could be the last one
left in the building to place the flyers on their desks.
He had closed his eyes and imagined each one of them
reading the following morning – caged birds waiting
to be released by the words and music of the Beatles.
And they counted the days they had left before their
big adventure. They would cross to Amsterdam to buy

their VW van, cushion and curtain its back into their
new nest and start moving through Europe, Africa and
the world.

The last few weeks in the house were painful; it had
been their universe and now they seemed to be the
only ones who were pleased to go. Inge shut herself in
her room where only the teenagers from the youth club
where she worked were allowed to come in; Simon
became even more absent than he had been before,
frantically dedicated to his deals in order to make the
money he would need for a deposit on his and Alice's
next destination; Paul was lost in a taciturn cloud,
sometimes looking at Ana with longing eyes, sometimes his red eyes filled with tears, sometimes his little
eyes hard and frightening. Juan and Ana spent more
time in their room now than they ever did in the six
months they had lived there; they huddled together
whispering secret plans which set them further and
further apart from those they had thought of as brothers and sisters such a short time before. Togetherness
and purpose had suddenly burst like a bubble, giving
way to squalor, the rancid smell of no direction, fear of
the future, phobias and depression.

They had come to this house as they had come
to all the others: through a friend of a friend, because
there was an empty room they could afford, because
they needed a roof over their heads. As usual, they
had not understood where they were or with whom;
they had felt open to all possibilities because nothing seemed worse than anything else. They were in
the land of the Who and the Rolling Stones – that is,
very very far away from home. They could not make
out the codes since they didn't even know about codes;
you learn about the existence of codes when you have
something to compare with, when you swim against
the current, when you have been rejected or discarded.
And for them this was still to come. So they did not
realize that for some this eviction was a tragedy, that
not everyone had wings to spread and fly; they could
feel the darkness that now surrounded them and they
were frightened of drowning in it.

The long stoned evenings in the sitting room had
become daunting. The pulse of the night that had
thumped through the speakers and kept them all in
tune with each other, that purring and glowing togetherness, had gone. Now they were a motley group of
scarred individuals, each one doubting their capacity

to make it safely to the following morning. When Inge finally emerged from her darkened and smoky room they saw her bulging belly but no one dared to mention it; her face and her seclusion already said that this was no cause for celebration, but part of a sequence of compulsion and self-recrimination, which would see to its own conclusion in some other house. Their visitors seemed to be the only ones who still had some flame in them; they continued to come and go and tell their stories while Simon quietly parcelled weed and counted their LSD tablets. This had become the only reassuring sign of normality in their jagged world where Paul's menacing figure cruised through the nights and slept through the days; they expected a catastrophe and they also wished for a miracle. Paul, the guardian of the house, had become its heart of darkness. Alice had always kept her grudge and her distance; she had never expected anything more than a momentary reprieve. Too many flats, too many men, too many moments of warmth had passed by her weary and beautiful face. For her the eviction was only what she already knew to be coming from the beginning, and in her presence Ana and Juan felt guilty of their own innocence.

On Christmas day the house was either empty or asleep. It was bitterly cold, a day on which they felt no excitement in hiding from other people's resentment. A truly desolate day when they wandered around the house looking for ways of quenching the physical pain of loneliness. It was hard to tell whether the unmade beds in the chaotic rooms had people in them or just their prints. Everybody had scattered, seeking human warmth and some reminder of family history or reassuring tradition. For Ana and Juan this day meant nothing more than a sense of foreignness. Paul was stirring in the kitchen, perhaps still up from the previous night, perhaps trying to make something of this special occasion. It was his idea that they should celebrate. 'Like every one else', he said. He made it feel like summer time then, like it had felt before they knew how different they were, when they thought they would always stay together. Ana, by her own account a keen animal lover, proposed the Zoo; the other two were happy to please her and after a last cup of tea they were on their way to the bus stop. The icy and dormant streets, the occasional family loaded with presents and carrier bags full of food, the few smug cars. They spent the next hour standing on their frozen feet and slapping their hands against their jackets until an old man

crossed the road to let them know that there were no
bus services on Christmas day, never had been, never
would be. Three convicts on bail, three orphans, three
heads in the cloud, three lost souls in London – they
returned home and turned the central heating on until
they baked, and they spoke about mothers and fathers
and cousins and aunts. It was a good Christmas.

When the month was up, the piano, like everybody
else in the house, had nowhere to go. They thought
that they should place a notice at the newsagent or
an ad in the local paper; they thought many different
things and perhaps they did try some of them, but the
piano, already there when Juan and Ana came into
the house, seemed to have no claimant. Perhaps as a
defiant gesture, perhaps as a metaphor, the piano was
therefore sentenced. Guests were invited to come with
their bare hands and throw the house out of the window
in the shape of an old ex-school-hall underused piano.
The large group gathered around their sacrificial lamb,
as if it represented the best in each one of them and,
when the first key was pulled off, it and they screamed.
Together they tore its neat ivory and black geometry,
their illusions, its hidden structure, their potential
tunes, while everyone sang and cried with each blow.

Some hid or covered their eyes or their ears; some said it was a 'happening' and they should have filmed it. Some died inside with the unwanted piano.

Perhaps nobody has ever told this story until this date – a story of rape, suicide and despair. A shameful story that brought the house together just to blow it apart like the last firework on a dark winter night. The following week Juan and Ana left for Europe, but Juan never distributed the flyers with the Beatles' song among the people he was leaving behind at work. By then he no longer knew if they really were flying.

TEN

Pregnant in Stamford Hill

In Kensington Square they suffocate under the weight of the surrounding Victorian buildings. As she descends the steps that lead to their small front door the air gets thinner by the second; under the low ceilings of that tastefully decorated bunker, Juan is already back from work; it is a seamless journey from the eight hours in the photographic darkroom, through the funnel of the London underground and straight into the darkness of their basement flat. She works as a sales assistant in Oxford Street, especially trained to blow the whistle on shoplifters and other wandering collectors – having been forced by her employers to buy the fashionable uniform out of her meagre wages. Refugees from the sixties, they have sat in communes' sitting-rooms losing track of time while listening to lucyintheskywithdiaaamonds, alongside dealers, delinquents, probation officers, burnt-out visionaries and the bobdylans of tomorrow; they have fallen asleep in the early hours of the morning, and – the joint lifted from between their fingers – woken up still in the same position with the light of dawn. They tried to open up their love to others, sometimes out of militant zeal, sometimes out of youthful polymorphic yearning; they thought they had found a family in exile; they thought they were bathing in the glow of love and peace.

Now they are alone again – as when they first arrived – scooped up in this elegant heart-of-London apartment, surrounded by wealth and history – the distilled essence of urban Englishness. Their landlady stoops every time they meet her on the narrow basement staircase, as if trying to bring herself down to the level where she places her lodgers. Coming down from her dwelling in the massive three-storey-house, she seems apologetic about their respective situations. Juan cannot stand straight when he walks under the low ceiling that extends from their kitchen to the bedroom – so he also stoops. Meanwhile Ana suffocates.

They are the proud owners of an ailing green Morris 1000 van; they have created an oriental tent at the back with patterned carpets from the Kensington skips and cushions covering the floor; no windows here either – but it moves and it's theirs. They love collecting their visiting parents from the airport, hunting for furniture from condemned houses, driving friends from Wales and youth club children from Camden.

When Juan and Ana reluctantly accepted the demise of their last commune they both felt secretly relieved to be alone with each other again. No more shares in other people's miseries – just their own. The little basement flat would become their nest, they thought; we will play mothers and fathers in the mini-kitchen and rock the bed with our lovemaking without always having to be overheard. And this is how the new project hatched – the baby project. She dreamt of it, yearned for it, made plans. Until then, she had not thought that a baby could happen to her, but overnight it became the only thing worth living for. No more other people's babies, which have so often come and gone; not nephews, whom she has adored and lost when they left on that boat, but a child to be in their lives for ever, to be one of them even before born.

They go for it with conviction if not passion: purpose kills sensuality, and more so does the repeated monthly

disappointment. It had not occurred to her before that
wanting and having could stand so far apart, and when
it finally happens, the real baby announces herself with
a further reduction in the air supplies: Ana feels more
suffocated than ever – and sick too. Without windows
she feels blind, and when Juan goes off to work every
day she is very alone with no parents or older sisters to
tell her what is going on inside her. She is on the brink.
Her guts have been blown up inside out and do not fit
within her skin; her despair meets with Juan's bewil-
derment and they are both quietly panicked. Now that
the baby is coming they want to run away – but there is
no place to hide. Lonely and foreign, they cannot gen-
erate a sense of home, as they had hoped they would.
Although they probably never put it into words, they
intuitively know that it will be necessary for them to
recreate a family for this baby to be born into. Like
migratory birds, they look around for human mud and
human straw with which to make a nest, and rest.

By the time her body embraces the growing baby, they
have left airless Kensington and are living in a new
commune in Stamford Hill. Perhaps the landlord – not
much older than they under his black hat, dark beard
and dreadlocks – did not expect that there would still

be hippies in 1972. Maybe Juan and Ana never looked like what they were trying so hard to be, but the fact is that, dressed in their best clothes, they have rented a house in the heart of Orthodox Jewry – and a fresh bunch of lost souls have rushed to take possession of the spare rooms: Kate who sleeps with her teddy bear, Theresa who sleeps with anybody who would want her, Walter who will commit suicide not many years later, David who trains to be a barrister but every weekend puts on his head-band and, tin-whistle in hand, takes to the streets bare-footed, Ben – provider of music and laughter, Catherine whose parents don't even know she is also expecting. Like Joseph and Mary, they find their manger.

This time love and peace do seem to take hold. The house purrs with good feeling. When no more empty rooms are left to accommodate yet another body, a new regime gets set up. Rooms will be divided according to function: the dorm, the changing room, the quiet room, the music room, the dining room, the love room... As food, clothes and records become common property, money begins to lose its meaning. The commune pools resources, they make big pots of milky porridge, they eat together in the evenings, they have pillow fights, they get stoned together in the evenings. The two mothers gather momentum and everybody becomes a child in this dreamy neverland. If time could be suspended, this would be the moment, a moment of relief and reparation for life to be reinvented according to a perfect dream. Sometimes Juan and Ana sleep in the dorm amidst giggles and snores; sometimes they occupy the quiet room holding each other and her big belly in between, waiting. This world they created, simply because they thought it already existed. They had heard about it in songs and seen it in the movies; they had come all the way from Buenos Aires to be part of it. It is a world of beautiful fiction where there is ample breathing space. It is just as it should be, as it is being right now. They embrace and wait, knowing and not knowing of its frailty. All willing participants are now on board: those who dream of mothering and those who pine to be mothered, all huddled together in no-man's land. They are surrounded by Orthodox Jewry that looks upon them just in the same way they themselves are looked upon: as bizarre, foreign, full of certainty. There is arrogance born of fear on both sides.

They rush into the ambulance with a sense of urgency and bemusement. Amongst the sea of anonymous black coats and wigs, their one and only Irish neighbour comes out to the street and, taking stock of the situation, lays his rough warm hand on the back of Juan's neck and says 'God bless'. Their own lot are too stoned to notice that Ana and Juan are at that very moment being borne out of the commune into the Autumn evening. The ambulance travels the bumpy journey across town to the only British hospital – this is still 1972 – that would allow Juan to hold Ana's hand and push with her while singing tengreenbottles through the increasing pain and panic at the sense of imminent and irreversible change. Night comes and goes, and so do mid-wives and student doctors, monitors, consultants and cheerful nurses. In the end, the pain is too frightening and there is a mad pethidine rush to the theatre. She will remember that particular part as having a ride on the ghost train at the funfair.

Their sweaty hands are locked together, their eyes fixed on each other's, tengreenbottles, their breath, the distant voices that shout 'push' ('like passing a melon', someone had said at the ante-natal class). And in the end here she comes, slithering through, face down, her dark hair stuck to her melonhead, soothing the passage and soothing their hearts as she emerges: that little perfect body. An awesome long silence follows, and then her voice, her unique and forever voice. From here on shitty nappies their possession, cries for their ears only, smiles for their eyes, and the light weight of her body just for their arms to nest. My, me, mine. Here childhood sheds and begins again. This skin, this warmth, this need. She, who changes the world irrevocably.

ELEVEN

Photograph

They are both looking at me now. One crouching, leaning against the brick wall; his head slightly tilted and his right arm resting on his knee, the other hand on her shoulder – if one could call it that. What I mean is that he has his hand over her, perhaps to gently encourage her to look in my direction while I am taking the picture. It is because she knows that he is right behind her, and that they are doing this together, that she appears to have no need to look at him at all. And although this is not really visible in the photograph, I am quite sure that she is sitting on his foot to make sure she can feel his every move and even his every breath. As for me, that is a different matter. There I am, behind the camera, reflected in their gaze, and also crouching because I want to be at the height from where she looks at the world. She observes me with patience, noticing my

unnatural behaviour: I am not walking, not seating
on a chair and not even lying on the floor. She passes
no judgment on the funny posture that I adopt when
I want to be on a level with her.

My son looks at the camera with a sense of occasion.
He wants this picture taken as much as I do. Together,
we have loved this creature for some years now, we
have shared our universe with her and, at times, we
have believed that we understood her a little and that
she too understood us. He looks at me like humans
look at each other when one of them holds a camera.
Through the lens I can see that he has not had enough
sleep last night, even though these days there is nothing new about that. I can see those bluish shadows
on his face that make it hard to locate his eyes – those
green eyes that I once thought I could read from. I can
see that although it is lunch time in the frozen moment
of the picture, he has not been up for long and yet he
has made the effort to come, rather than putting up
with my disappointment, or with me trying to guess
what exactly does he do with his life – now that he lives
away. And yet, although we have become strangers
in some ways, he still looks at me fully comprehend-
ing the matter that brings us together right now: our

tenderness for this companion who bonds us all with her sense of what it is to be part of the pack. My son and I know without words that, because of the assumptions that our dog so naturally makes about us all, we understand better the significance of our kinship. The photograph is a tribute to this citizen from another world, brought along by whim and by chance, who is so completely one of us. She, whose gift of simple thought and placid trust, commands reciprocity.

Alex the dog, who at this pictorial instant knows so precisely how to seat next to my son by the brick wall and how to look at my camera as if she knew what a camera is for, as if it made any difference. As if she actually grasped that there is a future when this memory will be held.

TWELVE

Lecture

I am teaching tonight. I am staring at the board in the
entrance hall of the college, to find out where I am supposed to give my seminar. I cannot see my name, and
I am not sure of the title; everything is hand-written
on it and there is too much to read. Eventually I find
my name in blue chalk; being short, it really should
have been easy for the scribe to get to grips with it, and
yet they have slightly smudged it and let it droop at the
end. But at least it says 'room 60' – so now I only need
to find out where that is. It is getting late.

As I travel the long corridor, having great difficulty
finding room 60, I have become increasingly aware
that I do not know what the seminar is about. Fortunately, the walk is extremely long, my steps hitting
hard on the floor, and by the time I finally get there

I seem to have come across the title: 'Life after 50
– Part I'. It has also become clear that 'Part I' means
between 50 and 70. I have a photocopied paper
under my arm that I expect the students would have
read for today. It is by two women whose names
I can vaguely recognize, and there are scribbles of
mine on the margins. This must mean that I have read
this paper before... perhaps when I taught last year,
or maybe when I was a student myself? And yet I have
to admit that I am not familiar with any of its contents. Never mind, I say aloud, this problem can be
overcome because, as it happens, I am fifty-five years
old and surely I should be able to talk with confidence
about this subject.

Arriving at the class-room I can see that the students are sitting around several tables untidily placed
together forming a long row. There are at least thirty
of them and, as I look at their faces, I realize that it
would be inappropriate just to speak about myself.
I don't seem to lose my cool though, and glancing at
the group I notice that they cover all ages: some are
younger and some are older than I am. I say to myself
that I will use their experiences for the seminar's discussion... Or was it, perhaps, a lecture?

I am now sitting, but the particular chair that they have left empty for me is in the middle of one of the long sides of the joined-up tables and I cannot see the faces of at least half of the students. In any case, I don't seem to get a proper view of those who are sitting across me either. With quite a confident gesture I leave my seat and take another one at the very head of the table. As I meticulously begin to take the papers out of my brief-case I notice that there is a man sitting with his back to me; since he too is facing the head of the table, it might well be the case that I have sat myself in what consti-tutes a second row. Many of the students are drinking tea from plastic cups, they talk with one another and seem distracted. All the same I proceed and say:

— Being fifty is horrible.

At this, some of the women sitting on the left side pro-test loudly:

— This is not what the authors wrote on the paper.

I respond with aplomb:

— I can say what I like.

I then notice that half the group has walked out of the room. I turn to the remaining students but, as I prepare to say something else, I realize that they are gathering their folders and leaving. Suddenly, I am completely on my own in this grimly lit place. I wonder whether I should inform the head of department about what happened or keep it to myself. While I am still sitting there a young, good looking woman wanders in. She is also a lecturer, coming to teach her seminar. We strike up a conversation and I begin to tell her what has just taken place. I can notice myself gradually relaxing and feeling better as I speak to her. Other youngish women come into the room – obviously some of her colleagues – talking amongst themselves. My young woman becomes distracted by them, and very soon she stops listening to me and begins to get ready for her own seminar, which is about to start.

THIRTEEN

ul. Sienna 38

Silence set its trap long before it was required – when there were no words to describe it and no need to speak. At the time, silence was not questioned – it was accepted as part of the family. Now, sixty years later, three old ladies wander around Warsaw bickering and blaming each other as if that could possibly change the past. The melancholic darkness, the loneliness that each had believed to be just her own, belong with the three of them like brown eyes and hair loss. Silence was mother's milk – they never really stood a chance against it. No happiness, no contentment or sense of decency could have possibly dug foundations on the unstable rubble of murder and regret.

It is cold, clean and bitter. It snows sideways when they have finally checked into the hotel and caught.

a taxi to ul. Sienna 38 – the one scrap of information gleaned from a letter in Polish that had been in their possession for the last twenty-five years. At Sienna 38, Warsaw, there was once a family home, a place which had photographs of their fresh childish faces framed in silver and displayed on the mantelpiece; a sitting-room where their names were mouthed and considered on their merits, maybe questioned or translated, possibly slightly mispronounced because much gets lost in translation. There was, at Sienna 38, a sense of entitlement, with all the warmth and the violence that this entails.

The taxi driver is glad to be released when he cannot find number 38. They step out of the car into the street and look up at the other numbers: 41, 43, 39. Across the road they walk up and down, mouths tightly shut to keep the snowflakes and the freezing air out. These are large square buildings, and empty spaces with no numbers; Sienna Street numbers its buildings only on one side of the road. The people at the travel agency where they go in to enquire – those lucky souls who can locate themselves at the call of 37 or 51 – have not even noticed their good fortune. Sienna 38 is another ghost, like grandparents, uncles and aunts, and photos on the mantelpiece. Sienna Street, they will learn later, was precisely where the wall was built and later destroyed, keeping all the even numbers inside the ghetto. That ghetto where they were always destined to belong. But for now, they walk the street in disbelief while the snow continues to fall; much later they drift towards the main road and hail taxis that never stop; thus in their father's birthplace they re-encounter that familiar feeling of alienation: no language, no reference, no history and no idea of how to get back to the hotel.

The plan to visit Poland had been routinely slotted into their conversation for as long as they are able to remember. In their childhood geography, Poland had been the centre of Europe: clocks were never slow there, trains arrived on time, men clicked their heels and kissed ladies' hands. And yet when two of them made their lives in Europe – another eternity ago – they managed to blank over Poland in their mental map. Cold, grim, and dark Poland was always postponed in favour of sunny Greece, Italy or Spain. Going home always meant a long trip to Buenos Aires, not the short hop to Central Europe that they have now taken, almost without discussion, perhaps driven by the unthought fear that they might die without ever breaking this silence.

Stranded in the Warsaw streets they join a sea of faces and words; the words can be made out but they do not open up; the faces too remain shut; they are like music without lyrics, which the sisters could just sit back and hum, if it weren't because it is still snowing, getting darker and colder by the minute. They had never thought before that cold could feel like fear. Later on, they will meet several Poles who will make a point of letting them know of their admiration for the Jewish mind and of their own history of humiliation and subjugation at the hands of the Germans and the Russians. For the moment they are simply shocked at the idea that their people, unknown and yet owned, could possibly have managed to stay alive for even one day in the Polish winter. But Gitla, Bernard, and millions of others kept themselves alive for days, months and years. Like the misery of a lonely baby, unbearable because the future is not conceivable, because there is nothing but the painful present – this must have been how it felt: a return to timelessness, to things being as they are for ever and to nothing else.

At the café they try to speak in all their original and acquired languages, but they only get back vacuous smiles and that music without lyrics which their father could not bear to pass on to them – his mother tongue. It continues to snow sideways. Is it ever possible to believe one's own history? Later on, their trip will bear fruit and they will learn about some of those they carry inside, those who are always on their shoulders. 'Deceased in 1944' – reads a document from Yad Vashem – so close to the time when there could have been a future! So near, and yet, by then, beyond imagination. As Gitla and Bernard were being submerged into timelessness, perhaps disbelief kept them alive a little longer. Now, the three sisters accept that two generations later nothing has changed much. Business, profession, money – all those categories that are easily confused with humanity – surely should have drawn a neat line over which brutality would not dare step. Until this trip, it had been possible to take refuge behind that thought: 'they suffered, they were discarded – but they were not really like us'. The shock for them is to realize how much they were 'like us', and how their lives were reduced to something they might have never believed they were capable of: surviving – no less, no more. No other moment of the journey

like this one at the café will bring the women closer to
those they never met, even if they have not yet found
out who they are. The pressure of not finding a way
back to the hotel, the blindness of having no language
and the bitterness of the cold: they collapse into dis-
cord and blame while sisterhood fragments into all its
different components.

Gitla met Jacob in 1900. He was ten years older, had
been to school and had become an engineer. That was
precisely what he was doing in her town: building
bridges in Silesia. It was a delight for both to discover
that the other one was also Jewish. Something that
could never be taken for granted when the families
were not from the same town and yet, in this case, what
would make their marriage possible.

    No mention of parents or siblings in the letters left
behind. Perhaps their families didn't really approve
of their marriage; perhaps they were already dead by
1931 – the date of the first letter found in Buenos Aires.
Jacob had died at fifty-seven from a heart attack. His
youngest son Wincent always feared that same fate.
Perhaps he thought he could escape a premature death
by running away; perhaps the gambling had already
started and he owed too much money in Warsaw;

perhaps he could not bear to be his mother's favourite and yet see his older brother Bernard getting ahead, being accepted at medical school, marrying another doctor. Wincent never explained how he appeared in Buenos Aires – although he once said that he chose it because it had the thickest daily newspaper he had ever seen. He always read two or three newspapers a day: one with breakfast, one in the armchair after lunch, and one lying in bed at night. In each of his three daughters he saw his mother's face. Perhaps his mother's face haunted him just like her letters did. Hit by widowhood and the financial crisis of the 30s, Gitla writes to her youngest son: 'I cannot pay the rent, you are my favourite, when are you coming back?'. Wincent, who wanted to see the world, who had galloped his horse against the Russians, who had a taste for expensive shoes and hats, who dreamt of riches and fancy hotels, now had two women to support: his new wife and their shared life in Argentina – a promise; and Gitla in Warsaw – waiting for his triumphant return to take his father's place and protect her from hunger and destitution.

These three old ladies, finally arriving in the hotel with wet shoes and frozen toes, these foreigners in their own

land, these three lost women. They are the babies that
clinched Wincent's fate. They are the ones that kept
him away from Gitla and also protected him from his
own youthful death – tying him to remorse and melancholy. They grew up listening to his silence and the
sighs that emanated from him at night; they looked
at him looking through them. Part of their father was
always far away.

Bernard's medical degree could do little for Gitla; her
daughter Rachel was in France already. But in the end
it made no difference because they were all drowning
in the raging war. And Wincent's promise to himself
that one day he would make up for his disappearance,
for the letters he didn't answer, for not holding his
mother in mind, became a true act of treason, an aban-
donment of the worst possible kind. Gitla languished
in the ghetto and died in Treblinka in 1942. Bernard
escaped from the Warsaw Ghetto with his wife – their
ten-year-old son already dead – and died at the hands
of the Nazis after joining the Polish Resistance. Rachel
and her husband fought with the French Resistance
and survived. Wincent fell into the depths of depression in Buenos Aires; he could not speak to his family

about his family, and he could not speak to anyone about his past. Does war ever end?

This is what the three sisters want to know. Each to her own life, they all seem dedicated to repairing the pain of others. Perhaps the way in which they find themselves living in different cities replicates their father's distance from Gitla, Bernard and Rachel. What they repeat is not really known to them because it was never spoken. Being so different, the three are nonetheless attached to their sadness, their guilt, their acute sense of what is wrong. They were nourished by their father's belief that expected from them what it did not expect from himself any more. He was like a wounded soldier in the battlefield, urging his companions to run for cover: 'Don't mind about me – save yourselves'. Maybe he would have wanted to hear those words from his mother and be redeemed. Spoken to his daughters, the words propel them to live honourable lives. But no redemption is really possible. Like him, they wanted to leave Poland behind and be part of a new world. It is hard to understand where the past belongs in oneself – especially someone else's past. Why do they start arguing about where they will have dinner tonight? Or cannot wait for each other before they set off to their next assignment? There is something bitter in these rows and at the bottom of each word the tongue licks a reproach. They are deaf to what is true in the other, accepting polite negotiation but admitting no concession. This is a tight operation because life is at stake. Death looks on.

Somebody should have known what to do, how to proceed, when Wincent finally understood that his family was steeped in the European war. His ignorance and his impotence humiliated him; the hole of distance filled in with shame. Already torn, here was another tug pulling at his fear and another one at his disbelief. In front of his wife, in front of his children, he was ripped apart by his own emotions. Perhaps he told himself that silence would protect others, perhaps he was too angry with those children that had kept him apart from his Polish family, perhaps he felt a coward and a failure. He couldn't speak and, instead, blank words moved over his heart. He brought up children who brought up children who live with this blank searching for the missing colour of the words lost in the Polish snow. Unknowingly.

Their borscht is served in the hollow of a bread loaf, the spoon scraping the gooey white into the intense beetroot red. Colour penetrates through the nose and it sets memory alight. Wincent used to click his tongue with delight when the cream was poured from above making a wind-world of pinks and whites in the large soup bowl. In spite of everything. In the late nights of Buenos Aires, he walked the streets singing Polish songs while his embarrassed children pretended they had never met him before, and yet watched him from the distance somehow knowing who was pacing with him in the dark. Being fed in this steaming restaurant in Poland stops the crying inside – and maybe this is how it was for him too. It is possible to walk with ghosts and we all do it when we can.

The three old ladies will part, they will return to their families in distant places. They will try to make life sparkle in those corners where there has only been white sound; they will populate the silence, and they will not heal. They will tell their children about their trip and their words will feel both empty and a little more owned. They will struggle not to forget. Some will search for signs of the dead; some will sit and write a story.

FOURTEEN

Epilogue

I was sitting in the canteen having a cup of tea. I am always sitting in the canteen but it is unusual for me to have a cup of tea, in the canteen or anywhere else. I don't really like tea. I used to like it when I was at home – a light amber, translucent syrup from Lipton's with three spoonfuls of sugar served in a glass tumbler. This is how my mother made tea for my father. I didn't get tea very often because it was expensive and because even then I always preferred coffee. But I used to like looking through the glass and watching my father sip with relish and sometimes click his tongue afterwards.

Tea at the canteen is a different affair altogether. It comes from a grey metal water can, but it is hard to imagine that there was ever any water involved in the making of it. It looks and it tastes thick and dark, even murky.

*Milk improves matters to some extent and it stops you
feeling that at the first sip your mouth will turn inside
out. I reckon that I must have been getting the flu because
that is the only occasion when I would ever want to risk
tea at the canteen.*

*So tea at the canteen it was. And reading the paper
at the same time. The place is always full and I didn't
want anybody sitting across the table, thinking that just
because we are looking at each other we should be finding
something to say. I do sometimes listen to the junk that
people talk when they sit at the same table in the canteen:
'How is it going then? What have you been up to? May
I sit here? Did you enjoy yourself at the weekend?'*

*The things that they say make it almost impossible for
the other person to find something to come up with next.
So everybody knows from the beginning that the conversation will spiral all the way down to the grim lino floor.*

*I was feeling cold and feverish, my ears burning and my
nose running, in no mood to look up. I had a pressure
on my chest that made me want to cough and splutter.
Come to think of it, this must have been the reason why
I was drinking tea, having read in some health section
of the newspaper that tea acts as a drying agent on the*

production of phlegm that makes you cough and splutter when you have a cold.

Not that it was doing me a lot of good. The coughing had been going on all morning and I was beginning to consider walking back home. I had also been aware of a sharp pain in my solar plexus and something like stitches under my shoulder blades. I was getting, I must confess, a little nervous about my condition.

I have been on my own since my wife passed away and it is only now that I notice how lonely it is to be a foreigner in a large city. My wife wanted us to have children and when that didn't work she thought we should go back home. But I didn't want the bother of her family and mine, all those parents and brothers and sisters, all those family quarrels and obligations.

'We are better off staying here', I used to say, 'better alone than in bad company', I would tell her... It just had not occurred to me that one of us would go first, and that it might be me who would be left to manage on my own. Well, the truth is that I didn't give much thought to what it is that one has to manage in order to keep going. The clothes, the food, the heat, the leaks, the smells.

Anyhow, there I was, coughing again with my head buried in the newspaper, when I thought I saw a shadow over my shoulder. I imagined that someone was about to talk to me, perhaps to enquire about my health, or even worse, to tell me that it was about time I took my germs home with me. So I pretended to be concentrating on the reading.

The next time I coughed I glimpsed something waving behind my other shoulder. I have always been scared of raids. I know that it is unlikely but, even after all the years of living in this country, I still fear that I will be picked up and taken by force to a seedy police station and beaten up until I confess something.

I carried on with my reading but I was sweating profusely and my glasses had steamed up. It was when I tried to keep still that I noticed the silence. Silence had gathered around me like a bubble. In that busy canteen where you have to shout to hear yourself think I could not hear a sound. I looked around and I encountered everybody's eyes on me, or rather, somewhere behind me. So I looked up and I saw my wings: long white feathery wings making slow ripples in the air, utterly sensitive to the layers of changing heat generated by my own and all the other bodies there, caressing my neighbours and their tables,

*brushing against the ceiling and the floor, and beginning
to lift me off my chair into a cradle of limpid air and out
of the suddenly wide open window.*

*The light was bright and cold. I shut my eyes tight and
hoped to be in my bed, head buried under the covers.
Surely that must have been where I was, still waiting for
the alarm to go off. Though I had to admit that the birds
were shouting particularly loud that morning, and that it
was draughty too... Perhaps the door to the balcony had
again opened in the middle of the night. I must do something about that before it gets really cold. Lighter still,
almost as if I was too tired even to draw the curtains last
night, or perhaps as if I had never made it to the bed and
I was sleeping on the floor of the lounge all night.*

*I don't make a habit of falling asleep in any old
place, although I must admit that lately it has happened
once or twice that anywhere is preferable to that crum-
pled empty bed. But not this morning, I thought, because
I could feel the rustle of the feathers around me, those soft
pillows that I finally bought for her on her last birthday.
I waved around, looking to catch one of them and put it
over my eyes to black out the brightness, but I have to say
that even the mattress had disappeared from under me.*

Vertigo made me startle. My eyes opened by themselves and all I saw was a dull white cotton texture around me. By now the screams of the birds were deafening and one even hit me with its feathery wing, rougher and tougher than I could ever had imagined.

I noticed that I had been waving my arms even though my wings seemed to be doing the job most efficiently. I was keeping up with the flock and nobody appeared to notice me: wind fast on my face, stomach like a fist, but still going.

Once I got into the rhythm of it I even heard myself screeching into the clouds and, although this might sound a little strange, I had this notion that her voice was in my ear. I became aware of a beady eye by my side that was keeping pace with me. I thought it could even be looking in my direction so I asked: 'Where are we going?' 'Home, home at last', I heard the eye say.

This first edition of *Time Secret* was finished
in June 2009.

It was typeset in 10.5/17 pt Monotype Imprint
with Adobe InDesign in a MacBook Pro and
printed with a Heidelberg Speedmaster –
the contents on 80 gsm Vancouver Book Wove
Cream vol 17.5, and the cover on 260 gsm Zeta
Laid board.

The book was designed and produced by
Carlos Sapochnik FISTD for Longstone Books